Christmas Songs

With special thanks to Ladybird Books Ltd., from whose **Christmas Songs** the idea for this matching music book originated.

Arranged by Barrie Carson Turner
Edited by Peter Foss
Cover artwork by Tricia Harrison
reproduced courtesy of Ladybird Books Ltd.
First Published 1988
© International Music Publications Limited
Southend Road, Woodford Green,
Essex IG8 8HN, England.

HAVE YOURSELF A MERRY LITTLE CHRISTMAS

Words and Music by
HUGH MARTIN and RALPH BLANE

JINGLE BELLS

Jin - gle bells, jin - gle bells, jin - gle all the way.

Oh, what fun it is to ride in a one-horse o - pen sleigh.

Jin - gle bells, jin - gle bells, jin - gle all the way.

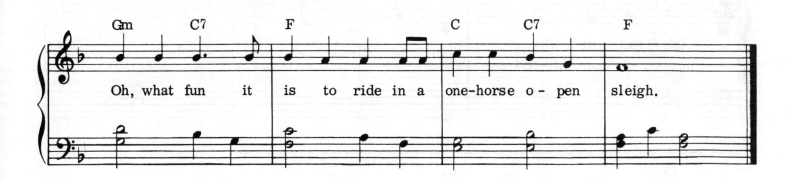

Oh, what fun it is to ride in a one-horse o - pen sleigh.

2. Now the ground is white
   Go it while you're young.
   Take the girls tonight,
   Sing this sleighing song.
   Get a bob-tailed bay,
   Two-forty for his speed.
   Then hitch him to an open sleigh
   And you will take the lead.
   Jingle bells, etc.

SANTA CLAUS IS COMIN' TO TOWN

Words by HAVEN GILLESPIE
Music by J FRED COOTS

ROCKIN' AROUND THE CHRISTMAS TREE

Words and Music
by JOHNNY MARKS

LET IT SNOW! LET IT SNOW! LET IT SNOW!

Words by SAMMY CAHN
Music by JULE STYNE

RUDOLPH THE RED-NOSED REINDEER

Words and Music
by JOHNNY MARKS

WE WISH YOU A MERRY CHRISTMAS

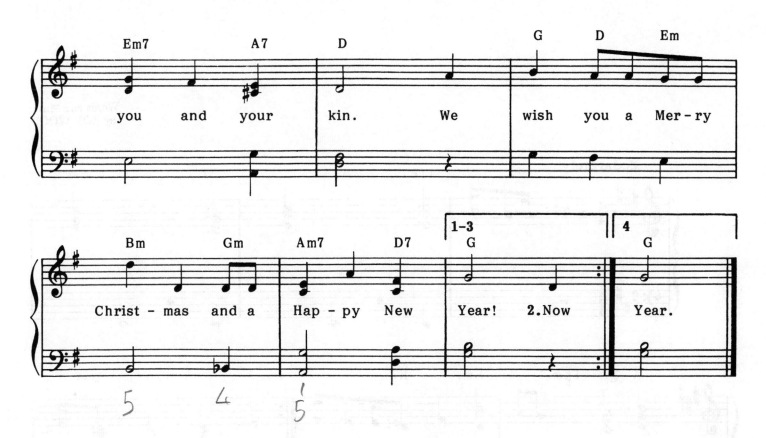

3. For we all like figgy pudding,
For we all like figgy pudding,
For we all like figgy pudding,
So bring some out here.
Good tidings we bring
For you and your kin.
We wish you a Merry Christmas
And a Happy New Year.

4. And we won't go until we've got some,
And we won't go until we've got some,
And we won't go until we've got some,
So bring some out here.
Good tidings we bring
For you and your kin.
We wish you a Merry Christmas
And a Happy New Year.

I WISH IT COULD BE CHRISTMAS EVERY DAY

Words and Music
by ROY WOOD

2. When we're skating in the park,
   If the storm clouds paint it dark,
   Then your rosy cheeks will light my merry way.
   Now the 'frosticals' appeared
   And they've frozen up my beard,
   So we'll lie by the fire
   Till the sleep simply melts them all away.
   CHORUS

3. When the snowman brings the snow,
   Oh well, he just might like to know
   He's put a great big smile on somebody's face.
   So if Santa brings the sleigh
   All along the Milky Way,
   I'll sign my name on the roof top
   In the snow then he may decide to stay.
   CHORUS

I SAW MOMMY KISSING SANTA CLAUS

Words and Music
by TOMMIE CONNOR

THE TWELVE DAYS OF CHRISTMAS

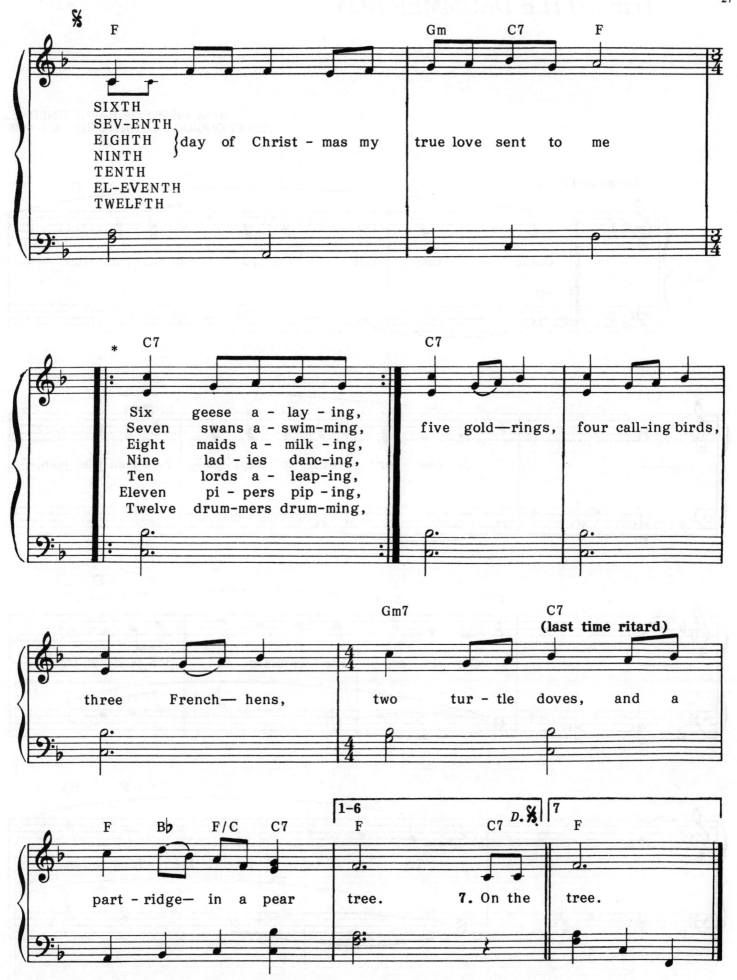

* Repeat this bar, in reverse order, as necessary

THE LITTLE DRUMMER BOY

Words and Music by HARRY SIMEONE,
HENRY ONORATI and KATHERINE K DAVIS

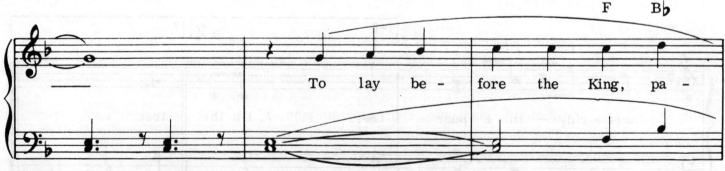

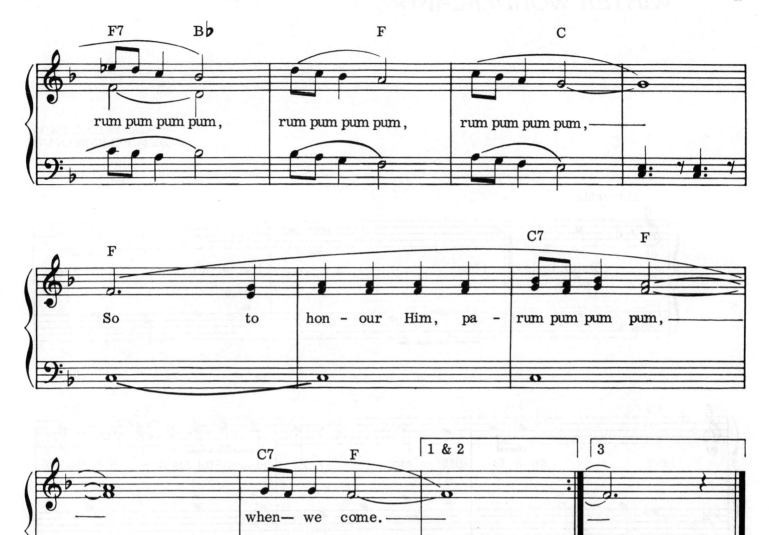

2. Little Baby, pa-rum pum pum pum,
   I am a poor boy too, pa-rum pum pum pum,
   I have no gift to bring, pa-rum pum pum pum,
   That's fit to give our King, pa-rum pum pum pum,
   Rum pum pum pum, rum pum pum pum,
   Shall I play for you, pa-rum pum pum pum,
   On my drum?

3. Mary nodded, pa-rum pum pum pum,
   The Ox and Lamb kept time, pa-rum pum pum pum,
   I played my drum for Him, pa-rum pum pum pum,
   I played my best for Him, pa-rum pum pum pum,
   Rum pum pum pum, rum pum pum pum,
   Then He smiled at me, pa-rum pum pum pum,
   Me and my drum.

WINTER WONDERLAND

Words by DICK SMITH
Music by FELIX BERNARD

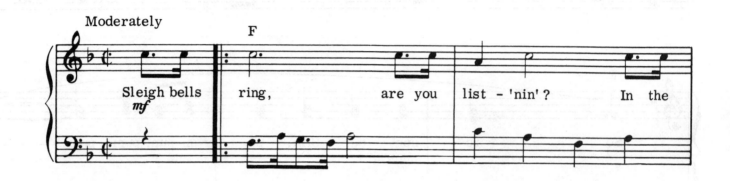

Moderately

Sleigh bells ring, are you list - 'nin'? In the

lane snow is glist - 'nin', A beau-ti-ful sight, — We're

hap - py to - night, — walk - in' in a win - ter won - der -

- land! Gone a - way is the blue - bird, Here to

SLEIGH RIDE

Words by MITCHELL PARISH
Music by LEROY ANDERSON

THE CHRISTMAS SONG
(Chestnuts Roasting On An Open Fire)

Words and Music by
MEL TORME and ROBERT WELLS

SNOWY WHITE SNOW AND JINGLE BELLS

Based on a theme by JOHNNY SHERIDAN, RALPH RUVIN,
HAROLD IRVING and DENNIS BERGER
By BILLY REID

Bright, with a bouce

41

CHRISTMAS ALPHABET

Words and Music by
BUDDY KAYE and JULES LOMAN

Bright, with a swing

"C" is for the CAN-DY trimmed a - round the Christ-mas tree.

"H" is for the HAP-PI-NESS with all the fam-i - ly.   "R" is for the REINDEER prancing

by the win-dow pane.   "I" is for the ICING on the cake as sweet as su-gar cane.

SILVER BELLS

Words and Music by
JAY LIVINGSTON and RAY EVANS

MARY'S BOY CHILD

Words and Music
by JESTER HAIRSTON

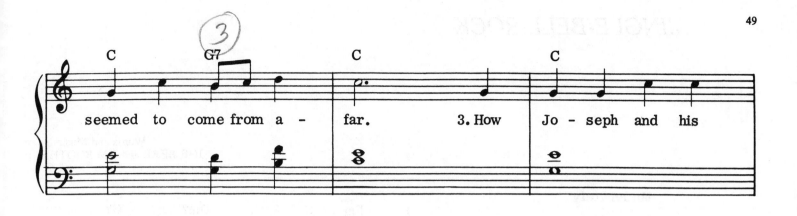

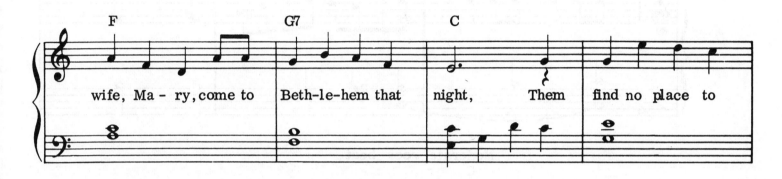

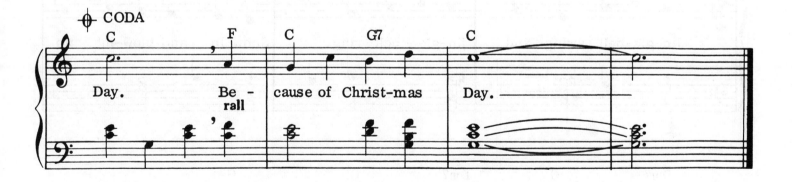

4. By and by they find a little nook
   In a stable all forlorn,
   And in a manger cold and dark,
   Mary's little boy was born.

5. Long time ago in Bethlehem,
   So the Holy Bible say,
   Mary's Boy Child, Jesus Christ,
   Was born on Christmas Day.

JINGLE-BELL ROCK

Words and Music by
JOE BEAL and JIM BOOTHE

Assigned 1959 to TRO Essex Music Limited, 19/20 Poland Street, London W1V 3DD

Printed by
Halstan & Co. Ltd., Amersham, Bucks., England